# PopularMMOS

Popular MMOS (aka Pat) is one of the most popular YouTubers in the world. Pat and his wife, Jen (aka Gaming With Jen), created their Minecraft-inspired channel, PopularMMOS, in 2012. Since then, they have entertained millions of fans around the world with their gaming videos and original characters.

Pat and Jen live in Florida with their cat, Cloud. *PopularMMOS Presents A Hole New World* is their first book.

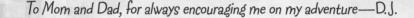

*To Mom and Dad, for always encouraging me on my adventure—D.J.*

A special thanks to Joe Caramagna for all his creative help!

PopularMMOs Presents A Hole New World  Text copyright © 2018 by PopularMMOs, LLC. Illustrations copyright © 2018 by Dani Jones. All rights reserved. Printed in the United States of America. No part of this book may be used or reproduced in any manner whatsoever without written permission except in the case of brief quotations embodied in critical articles and reviews. For information address HarperCollins Children's Books, a division of HarperCollins Publishers, 195 Broadway, New York, NY 10007.
www.harpercollinschildrens.com

Library of Congress Control Number: 2018934063
ISBN 978-0-06-279087-3 (trade bdg.)
ISBN 978-0-06-284639-6 (special edition)
ISBN 978-0-06-287868-7 (special edition)

The artist used an iPad Pro and the app Procreate to create the digital illustrations for this book.
Typography by Erica De Chavez  18 19 20 21 22  LSCC  10 9 8 7 6 5 4 3 2 1  ❖  First Edition

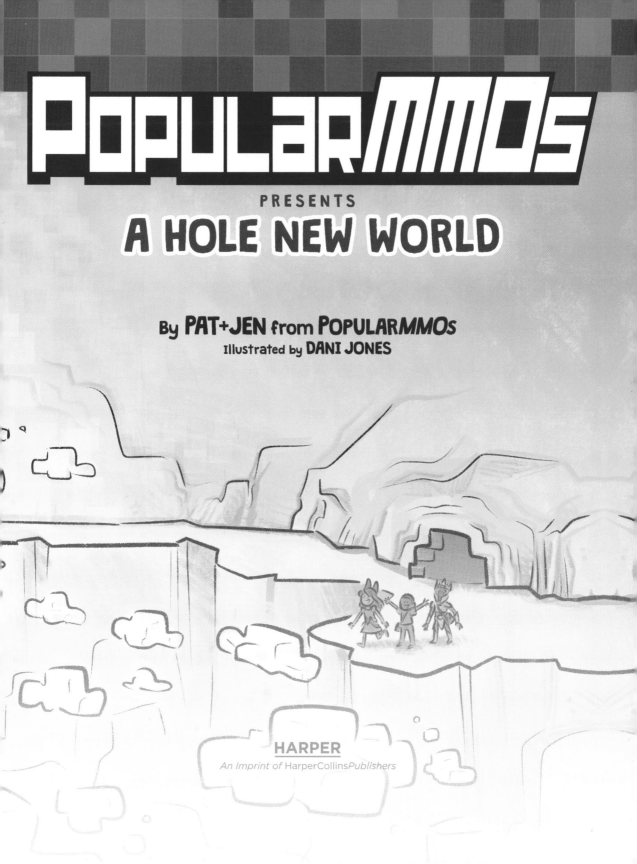

# POPULARMMOS

PRESENTS

## A HOLE NEW WORLD

By **PAT+JEN** from **POPULARMMOS**
Illustrated by **DANI JONES**

**HARPER**
*An Imprint of HarperCollinsPublishers*

Hey, what's going on, guys!

It's Pat, and welcome to my first book! If you've ever seen my videos, then you know that I love playing games and creating my own characters, from Bomby to Captain Cookie and, best of all, Evil Jen. For the past couple of years, I've been lucky enough to be able to share all the thrilling quests that my characters have embarked on through my YouTube channel, but this graphic novel lets me take our stories to a whole new level.

Now my characters can go on an epic adventure the likes of which I could only ever create in these pages. With a magical unicorn, an army of zombies, and a dangerous underworld, our heroes are trying to escape the hole new world that comes straight out of my imagination.

Wherever your own imagination happens to take you, I hope this book sparks your own creativity.

# PAT & JEN

Pat is an awesome dude who's always looking for an epic adventure with his partner, the Super Girly Gamer Jen. Pat loves to have fun with his friends and take control of every situation with his cool weapons and can-do attitude. Jen is the sweetest person in the world and loves to laugh, but don't let her cheeriness fool you—she's also fierce. In fact, she could be an even greater adventurer than Pat . . . if she weren't so clumsy. Together, along with their cat, Cloud, they have a bond that can never be broken.

# CLOUD

Cloud is Pat and Jen's white Persian cat. He may have a fluffy exterior, but underneath, he's all *savage*.

# CARTER

Carter is Jen's best friend and biggest fan, but he doesn't seem to like Pat very much at all. Carter is also not very smart and is known for carrying a pickle that he thinks is a green sword! But Carter means well, and if Pat and Jen hope to survive, they're going to have to trust him.

# CAPTAIN COOKIE

No one is quite sure if Captain Cookie is a real sea captain or if he just dresses the part. He doesn't seem to be very good at anything, but that doesn't stop him from bragging about how great he is! He's rude to everyone he meets but always in a funny way.

# MR. RAINBOW

Mr. Rainbow is a magical sheep whose wool can appear to be any color of the rainbow. He's the leader of the resistance against Evil Jen's tyranny and arms his friends with mystery boxes that contain secret weapons!

# GIZMO

Gizmo is a magical unicorn who leaves a trail of rainbows wherever he goes!

# HONEY BOO BOO

Honey Boo Boo is a golem of iron on the outside but is all softy on the inside!

# BOMBY

Bomby is somewhat of a pet to Pat and Jen but also Pat's best friend. You can usually find him by following the craters left by the TNT that he loves to watch explode. He doesn't talk, but when he goes missing, the adventure that follows speaks volumes for how much he is loved by everyone.

# EVIL JEN

Evil Jen's favorite thing is chaos. She lives for wreaking havoc on the world. What makes her truly evil, however, is that she would take someone as sweet as Jen and become an evil version of her. She even looks *exactly* like her (just don't tell Jen we said that!).

NOOoOOoOOOOO!

THUNNK!

UHN!

UH-OH.

BADUM BADUM BADUM BADUM